OILS +
SCRIPTURE

a modern perspective on ancient tools

by Erin Rodgers

Oils + Scripture
Erin Rodgers
V1/11-2018
©2018 Oil Supply Store LLC
Published by Oil Supply Store, LLC
Knoxville, TN

To purchase copies of this book please visit OilSupplyStore.com or ErinRodgers.com

contents

A letter from Erin

Hey friend!

I'm so excited to be on this journey as we dive in together to learn about essential oils and what Scripture has to say about them. Spoiler :: not much, and yet TONS all at the same time. Stay tuned; there's so much to learn together!

I began using essential oils from Young Living Essential Oils in 2014 and was astounded at how effective and awesome they were for our family. I immediately began sharing them with friends and family and at some point started to dig into what the Bible meant with all these vague mentions to plants and recipes.

After combing books, presentations, old files, and listening to friends tell their stories, I cobbled together my first "class" which I titled "A Biblical Perspective on Essential Oils." Not a unique title, but it worked.

While teaching that class, I wept.

I listened to the crinkly pages of Scripture turning through that room as nearly a hundred friends gathered to learn together.

We poured over Scripture.

We cried over Scripture.

And I heard the Lord whisper softly to me, "Hey Erin... THIS. This is why."

It's taken me a few years to figure out what to do with that, but a couple weeks ago I sat at my desk and dove into Scripture to update and rework that class. I quickly found myself exclaiming, "what in the world!!!" and "are you kidding me right now??!" and once again crying over the Bible and God's provision for us.

I sheepishly explained to my husband, Bronce, that I felt the Lord calling me to put these notes into book form so that class notes could stretch further than our own team of JoyDroppers and others could benefit from the research hours I've put in, and was humbled when he told me he'd been thinking the same thing and encouraged me to start immediately. Um. Okay, honey. Eek.

Well, here we go.

This book you hold in your hands is the result of hours of study and the encouragement of sweet friends. Hopefully it honors the efforts of many leaders who went before me with the desire to get these oils in every home.

Before we get started, let me pray over you and me together.

Heavenly Father, Lord,

Thank you for the gift of your Word. Thank you for the way you've laid out the plan of redemption. Thank you for taking care of our every need. I pray that we would discern your truths from Scripture and I pray that I have accurately represented those truths on these pages. Father, if I've misspoken, let the words fall right off the page. I want nothing but Your Goodness and Mercy to shine through the story told here.

I pray a special blessing over the friend reading this book right now. Help them learn and understand the Truth as You have designed it.

Father, I thank you for allowing my simple life to be a vessel for your Goodness. I thank you for letting me teach others about You and pray I've done it well here. Lord, to YOU be the glory. Now and forever.

Amen

Okay. Now y'all ready to dive in?

Unless I specify otherwise, I'm quoting the New International Version of the Bible. I also use BibleHub.com a ton because they have digitized access to a super cool lexicon, Strong's Concordance, and all the clicky links to dive deep into word history -- which I totally geek out on.

So if you're ready, let's go!

xoxo - *Erin*

Good Gifts from a Good Giver

When I first encountered oils as a tool for my family's health, I quite simply thought "Plants, yep. God made plants and called them 'good.' I bet we can benefit from them. Let's see how they can help."

I will be honest, I never questioned using plants for our health. I don't believe the God of the universe handed us plants for nourishment and then later said, "but wait, you can't use these for healing." Over the years I've heard questions regarding essential oils being part of questionable religious beliefs or used as part of new age practices. This has always driven me to the Word to confirm what I felt to be true.

I believe that we have a Heavenly Father who provided for all our spiritual and physical needs at the time of Creation.

Through John 1:1-5 we know that Jesus was present from the point of Creation, showing that from the very beginning God had a plan to rescue us from sin. In that same way, we know that God placed Adam and Eve in a GARDEN and subsequently charged him with managing the plants. This shows He had a plan to help us and heal us before He created us.

So if you've been asked those questions or are in a season where you're asking yourself those things, let me first say this: all Christians who love God must defer to His word and the way the Holy Spirit is speaking to us through the Word and our own lives.

I truly believe that plants are available for our health and healing and find no issue with that. But I also know that others may feel strongly another way or have a different experience and I honor their right to feel that way.

Just like I can never argue someone into believing the words of Jesus are true, I cannot argue with someone who is convinced that the use of essential oils is wrong.

In that case, I'm saddened but it does not affect my own walk with the Lord or use of oils in our home. Just like Paul said in 1 Corinthians 6:12, "'I have the right to do anything,' you say--but not everything is beneficial. 'I have the right to do anything'--but I will not be mastered by anything." Using plants for our healing is certainly permissible, but if it were an area where I was being mastered by those oils, I would walk away.

I believe that essential oils are one of the many beautiful gifts from our Good Giver. While I have found them to be a phenomenal resource for our family's health, I don't worship the oils, I worship the Lord. My focus of admiration is on the Gift Giver, where I believe the power rests, not on the gift itself.

As those who hold Biblical wisdom above all else, modern Believers have learned to be skeptical of other belief systems that might seek to twist Scripture around to further their own agenda. Unfortunately, in the process it's common to scoff at a gift from our Giver out of fear or misunderstanding.

Ahhhh, sweet friends. Let's embrace these gifts together! Let's focus on the Lord and on His healing in our lives. Let's dive in, research together, and commit to learn prayerfully and with an open mind! I pray I never overlook a gift from our faithful Giver!

"In the beginning was the Word, and the Word was with God, and the Word was God. He was with God in the beginning. Through him all things were made; without him nothing was made that has been made. In him was life, and that life was the light of all mankind. The light shines in the darkness, and the darkness has not overcome it."
John 1:1-5

What are Essential Oils?

Essential oils are often called the "life blood" of a plant. They're the liquid that flows inside a plant to protect it from harm and deliver nutrients. These amazing bottles of plant juice are distilled from the leaves, stem, flower, and roots of plants.

When you walk through the woods and smell the trees, or tear a leaf open and feel the liquid inside, this is the essential oil you're experiencing. Plants were part of God's provision for us in Biblical times, and they're part of His provision for us today.

Essential oils are not greasy. Instead, they quickly evaporate and are able to penetrate quickly through our skin into our body, are accessible through aromatic use, and are beneficial through ingestion.

When distilled and bottled properly, essential oils are a powerful part of a family's tools for health and wellness. Historic uses for oils are still relevant today and rising in popularity in our culture.

Essential oils and fatty, carrier oils serve different but complimentary purposes.

- Fatty oils like coconut, almond, olive, or grapeseed oil (which we often refer to as a "carrier" oil) are pressed or chemically expelled, but essential oils are distilled from the plant parts.

- Fatty oils are usually necessary for the seed to germinate and sprout but are not necessary for the life processes of the plant beyond that germination. Essential oils typically aren't involved with early growth of the plant but are essential to the life processes of the plant.

- Fatty oils are large, non-aromatic and nonvolatile molecules, while essential oils are tiny, aromatic, and volatile. Essential oils circulate throughout plants and in the human body, while fatty oils don't circulate or pass through tissues, cell walls, or cell membranes.

How To Use Oils

Topically
- Follow bottle's dilution recommendations
- Using a carrier oil, apply topically with fingers or a roll-on bottle

Aromatically
- Directly inhale from the bottle
- Use a few drops in your diffuser
- Put 1-2 drops on a cotton ball, place in car or home air vents

Internally
- Put several drops of essential oil into an empty vegetable capsule & take with water
- Add a few drops to a glass of water or rice milk
- The Vitality line of oils are labeled for internal/dietary use

Oil Safety

Carrier oils ensure that essential oils applied topically are comfortable to the skin. Dilution with a carrier oil does not dilute the effect of the essential oil. In fact, it prevents waste due to excessive application or essential oils' evaporation.

It is recommended that you always dilute when you're unsure about a new oil or when using oils with children. Dilution recommendations can be found on your Young Living bottles!

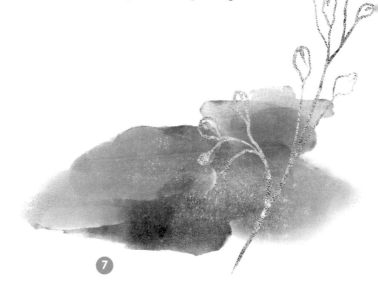

Oils in History & Scripture

In Genesis we read about God creating the garden and then creating Adam and Eve. I love that God was the original gardener. Genesis 1:29 states, "then God said, 'I give you every seed-bearing plant on the face of the whole earth and every tree that has fruit with seed in it. They will be yours for food.'"

Essential oils were spoken into existence when God created the original plants, and he gave them to man for nourishment.

Essential oils have been used throughout history to support health and wellbeing. One of the oldest known medical records supports this. Ebers Papyrus is an Egyptian document dating back to 1550 BC (and even THAT copy is recognized as a copy of a much older original!) and records over 700 recipes and protocols using plants for therapy. Egyptian tradition used oils for healthcare, perfume, and even for embalming bodies -- even their pharaohs were buried with vats of oils, showing their cultural importance.

Steam distillation was a process used by Babylonians, Chinese, East Indians, Egyptians, and Sumerians as far back as 3500 B.C. The technology was disappearing around 1000 B.C. and gone by the fall of Rome in 500 A.D. Persians rediscovered this technique centuries later.

Our ancient counterparts relied on their oils for baths, healing, perfumes, and anointing. God gave the Israelites directives that included plants we can still access and test for healing properties.

Modern technology allows us to control the temperature of steam distillation to within a fraction of a degree, unlike the inconsistent fires our ancient friends used. We are able to test for the brix (carbohydrate level) of a plant before cultivating it. Advancements in farming and technology ensure our essential oils are better than those of the past.

And if they were amazing tools for wellness and anointing thousands of years ago, with our modern adaptations they are certainly even better now!

Depending on your translation, "oil" is specifically mentioned 191 times in the Bible, but there are over 600 references to essential oils and/or the 33 species of plants they come from. Essential oils are referred to as "fragrances," "odors," "ointments," "aromas," "perfumes," or "sweet savors."

While oils are mentioned IN Scripture, the Word doesn't contain many details about their practical and day-to-day use. For those details, we must look elsewhere. I had a moment when this caused me to ask personally, "um... so if the Bible doesn't tell me HOW to use them... were they even important in Biblical times?"

Remember, the Bible is full of letters, poems, and recorded history, not a resource for the basics of everyday life.

Let's examine this from a modern perspective. If I were to write an email to my best friend, I could mention a host of medications by name that would make sense to her without explanation. "I took a ___ before I went to bed" could easily explain without words the symptoms I was feeling, and she would assume the dosage without needing more information.

I wouldn't explain those unnecessary details in an email or text because it would be understood by my audience. In the same way, the writers of the Old and New Testaments didn't often give specificity to their usage or amounts when mentioning plants used for healing. Therefore, we can't discount their importance, but we may need to consult other references to determine the specifics of use.

Thankfully, a host of records that exist with that information! It is through careful consideration of historical references that we have come to the knowledge we have currently.

Sometimes when Scripture doesn't explain the details, our study of the Bible serves as a jumping-off point for us to do extra research about life during that time period. The common mention of essential oils in Scripture has allowed that for me! It's fun to research more!

A Bit of Chemistry

Throughout the last 30-40 years, modern distillation has become an enrapturing art and science. We are constantly learning new things about these plants our ancient friends used for healing.

We can largely thank D. Gary Young for the years of research and dedication to essential oils and developing the only true Seed to Seal method of cultivating plants for distillation. If you've never read the book *D. Gary Young, The World Leader in Essential Oils*, get a copy now! It's available through Young Living or through Life Science Publishers.

Starting in the 1900s, scientists were able to isolate certain compounds in essential oils to better understand how they impacted our bodies and the benefits they could offer.

Of course, with that scientific advancement comes the desire to create cheaper alternatives to our precious oils by altering compounds in inferior plants or by "doctoring them" with lab-created alternatives.

Creation can't be replicated in a lab, friends. Nope.

One drop of oil contains 40 million trillion molecules.

Here's that number: 40,000,000,000,000,000,000

That's a lot of zeros! Our bodies contain about 100 trillion cells... So any single drop of essential oil can cover every cell in our body with tens of thousands of life-giving molecules!

This helps explain why simply inhaling our oils can have a significant impact on our health over time.

If you wish to dive in to additional chemistry like phenols & phenylpropanoids, monoterpenes, and sesquiterpenes, I highly recommend it! There is so much to learn that will enhance our understanding and use of essential oils.

These oils are intricate and powerful in so many ways and point back to the genius and brilliance of our Creator God!

"Lord, our Lord, how majestic is your name in all the earth!

You have set your glory in the heavens.

Through the praise of children and infants you have established a stronghold against your enemies, to silence the foe and the avenger.

When I consider your heavens, the work of your fingers, the moon and the stars, which you have set in place, what is mankind that you are mindful of them, human beings that you care for them?

You have made them a little lower than the angels and crowned them with glory and honor.

You made them rulers over the works of your hands; you put everything under their feet: all flocks and herds, and the animals of the wild, the birds in the sky, and the fish in the sea, all that swim the paths of the seas.

Lord, our Lord, how majestic is your name in all the earth!"

Psalm 8

Emotions and the Brain

For a long time, scientists believed our brain was plastic, unchangeable. Any damage done to our brains was believed to be irreversible.

However, the current field of neuroscience is blasting through those long-held beliefs, and we can learn a great deal from this.

I'm a big fan of the research of Caroline Leaf. She's a cognitive neuroscientist with a PhD in Communication Pathology and a Bachelor of Science in Logopedics and Audiology, specializing in metacognitive and cognitive neuropsychology. (Ummmmm. She's SMART, y'all!)

Dr. Leaf weaves Brain Science and Scripture together, confirming Proverbs 23:7 "For as he thinks within himself, so he is" (NASB).

Romans 12:2 reads, "Do not conform to the pattern of this world, but be transformed by the renewing of your mind." Could we, in fact, renew our mind? Is it within our power to make changes to the way our brain works?

> "That the brain is plastic and can be changed moment by moment by how we direct our thinking – in other words, the choices we make – is a top idea on the bestseller list, and it actually is the key to switching on our brains. Add to this the fact that every morning when you wake up, new baby nerve cells have been born while you were sleeping that are there at your disposal to be used in tearing down toxic thoughts and rebuilding had a healthy thoughts. The birth of these new baby nerve cells is called neurogenesis, which brings to mind "The Lord's mercies… are new every morning "(Lamentations 3:23).

> "What a remarkable and hopeful portrait of the endless adaptivity of the human brain God has given us" (Leaf 24).

Scripture paints a picture of our emotional wellbeing changing our physical outlook. And it often links our emotions to a fragrance!

Aroma and Emotions

Aroma works in our brains in a number of ways. One is by recall. Ever walk into a home that "smells like grandma" and in a flash your mouth waters for the apple pie your grandmother always had ready when you visited?

For me, a certain smell takes me right back to stepping in my great-grandmother's house, and I immediately get a craving for the Italian cookies she always hid in the cabinets for my brother and me to sneak when Mom wasn't looking.

In many ancient religious cultures, foot washing was a sign of welcome for a guest in one's home. It was customary to provide a bowl of water to let your visitor wash his feet - or in some cases for the host to do the washing themselves or through the provision of a servant. Foot washing was often necessary for cleanliness in dusty regions where travelers wore sandals. In many cases, it was followed with a covering of oil. These oils were beneficial for the guest and the aroma made for a welcoming environment.

Just like an aroma might take you back to a childhood memory, the oils used on a guest can remind them of being welcomed into another happy home and bring a smile to their face.

Beyond recalling a memory, aromatic components have been used historically for mental, physical, and spiritual healing. Countless studies have shown that the inhalation of aroma has a profound effect on human brain functions, including altering cognition, mood, and social behavior.

We diffuse in our home to create a welcoming environment. When hosting guests, I often think through the oils we use in our main rooms as well as specially choosing a few singles or blends to put by the diffuser in our guest bedroom. Some of my favorites are single oils such as Frankincense or Cypress, or blends like Joy, Valor, Christmas Spirit, or Sacred Mountain - which contain several biblical oils and are well loved!

Therefore, if emotions can heal our brain, and aroma can affect our emotions... let's keep sniffing those oils!

Healing in the Bible

The Bible includes many examples where God has the power to heal our physical bodies. While we often think of this in terms of a miraculous, instantaneous healing, that's not the primary way the Israelites would have viewed healing.

The first "healers" among the people were the priests. While there are some early scriptural references to doctors, in large part the people trusted their health to their priests.

The Lord links our spiritual, emotional, and physical health all together; it's only our modern medical system that has chosen to treat them all as separate pathways. Because of that, the priests of the Old Testament had the major responsibilities for diagnosing and prescribing remedies for the people. Childbirth was regulated to midwives, though.

Biblical priests had many jobs...

- they led worship -- offerings, sacrifices, & prayers
- they served as spiritual counselors & heard confession
- they were judges who enforced the ecclesiastical law
- they were keepers of the perpetual fire that burned day and night to honor God
- they were responsible for certain medical diagnoses and treatments
- they were apothecaries & perfumers, mixing various oils and herbs for anointing, incense, and healing
- they were responsible for the grounds around the temple
- overall, they served as models of exemplary and righteous living

Wow. That is a longer list than we often realize when reading the Old Testament. I fear we have underestimated the role of the priest.

While Exodus provides instructions to the priests who served the Israelites, the New Testament reveals a different story.

In 1 Peter 2:9 we read, "But you are a chosen people, a royal priesthood, a holy nation, God's special possession, that you may declare the praises of him who called you out of darkness into his wonderful light."

So WE are the priests of today.

What does that mean, exactly?

2 Corinthians 6:16 says, "For we are the temple of the living God. As God has said: 'I will live with them and walk among them, and I will be their God, and they will be my people.'"

Friends, as followers of Jesus, WE are the temple. The Spirit of God resides in our very being.

I challenge you to think of the Old Testament priest's role at the left in terms of our own role as priest.

It is humbling to submit to the Lord's design in this way, but it is a challenge we must accept. We must worship. We must maintain our temples. We must keep alight the fire in our hearts that honors the Lord.

Take some time and read through these Scriptures about the New Testament temple.

1 Peter 2:4-12

1 Corinthians 3:16-17

1 Corinthians 6:12-20

2 Corinthians 6:16-18

Prayerfully consider how you are caring for your temple. Are there any specific things from the list at the left that need to be a focus in this current season?

Three Kinds of Healing

While the English language has one word -- "heal" -- the original Greek had three root words which have all been translated into the English "heal." However, the Greek words have three distinct meanings in their original language.

Sozo is used over 100 times in the Bible and is often directly translated as *salvation*, though it can also be translated as *heal*. The Strong's Concordance defines this as "deliver out of danger and into safety, used principally of God rescuing believers from the penalty and power of sin -- and into His provisions." This deliverance refers to a total restoration of body, spirit, and soul.

One familiar use of *Sozo* is in John 3:16-17, "For God so loved the world that he gave his one and only Son, that whoever believes in him shall not perish but have eternal life. For God did not send his Son into the world to condemn the world, but to save [*sozo*] the world through him."

Iaomai is a Greek word used 27 times in Scripture and refers almost exclusively to the supernatural healing Jesus performed to bring attention to Himself as the Great Physician.

Sometimes Jesus healed with a touch, but other times He healed with His words as we read in Matthew 15. In this chapter, a Canaanite woman begs Him for mercy on her demon-possessed daughter. In verse 28 Jesus says to her (oh and I can just imagine the joy in His voice with this!), "Woman, you have great faith! Your request is granted." The verse continues, "And her daughter was healed [*iaomai*] at that moment."

I so want to be a woman of such deep, trusting belief that the Lord exclaims, "Woman, you have great faith!"

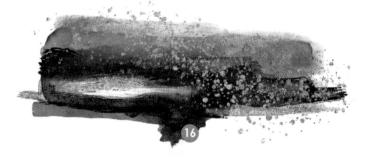

Therapeuo is the third kind of healing, mentioned over 40 times in Scripture. According to Strong's Concordance, it means "reversing a physical condition to restore a person having an illness (disease infirmity)." It is the root word of "therapy" and typically involves natural elements in the process of healing.

I love this analysis from *Healing Oils of the Bible* by Dr. David Stewart PhD:

> In Mark 6:13 where Jesus instructs his disciples to "anoint the sick with oil and heal them," the healing word is "therapeuo." In Luke 10, where Jesus gives instructions to "seventy others" to "heal the sick," the word is "therapeuo." In Revelation 22:2 where it says, "The leaves of the trees shall be for the healing of the nations," the word is, again, "therapeuo." God does not ask that we do miracles (iaomai). He only asks that we care for the sick (therapeuo) and help them find healing by applying His natural medicines (91-92).

We must remember that God provides the healing. Whether over time or instantly, it is healing that ultimately comes from Him. We need to keep applying our oils. We must keep praying. We should anoint others and bless them.

Jesus' ministry was to care for the weak and broken. We are now able to join Him and be a part of what He did while here on earth. Some are broken in body and others are broken in spirit. We have tools at our disposal to help and heal.

"The thief comes only to steal and kill and destroy; I have come that they may have life, and have it to the full."

John 10:10

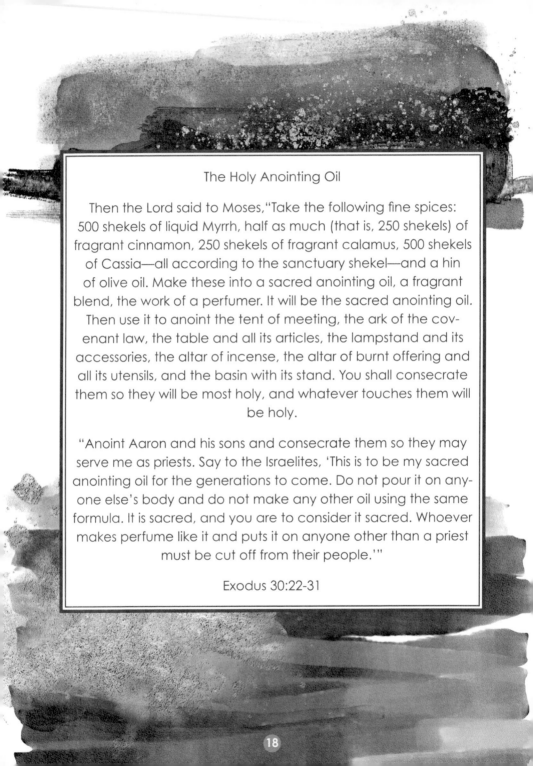

The Holy Anointing Oil

Then the Lord said to Moses,"Take the following fine spices: 500 shekels of liquid Myrrh, half as much (that is, 250 shekels) of fragrant cinnamon, 250 shekels of fragrant calamus, 500 shekels of Cassia—all according to the sanctuary shekel—and a hin of olive oil. Make these into a sacred anointing oil, a fragrant blend, the work of a perfumer. It will be the sacred anointing oil. Then use it to anoint the tent of meeting, the ark of the covenant law, the table and all its articles, the lampstand and its accessories, the altar of incense, the altar of burnt offering and all its utensils, and the basin with its stand. You shall consecrate them so they will be most holy, and whatever touches them will be holy.

"Anoint Aaron and his sons and consecrate them so they may serve me as priests. Say to the Israelites, 'This is to be my sacred anointing oil for the generations to come. Do not pour it on anyone else's body and do not make any other oil using the same formula. It is sacred, and you are to consider it sacred. Whoever makes perfume like it and puts it on anyone other than a priest must be cut off from their people.'"

Exodus 30:22-31

Oils in Exodus

The Lord was so precise and specific in the way He instructed the Israelites to create the Holy Anointing Oil. He gives them a specific recipe to follow and then instructs them that this oil is only to be used on priests, not lay people.

It can be so easy to skim these passages in Scripture, hunting for the "meat" of the Word. After all, what can we learn from an ancient recipe from an ancient practice?

Oh friend. It is so fascinating to read of God's care for His people, and this is an excellent reminder.

Let's unpack this together.

In Exodus 30 we find the Israelites involved in a massive caravan (estimates put their numbers around 2.4 million people!) as they've left Egypt and are meandering around the desert on their way to the Holy Land. Because of their constant disobedience and disregard of the Lord's directives, they continue to wander.

God was specific in the way he instructed the Israelites to make this blend of oil—there was purpose and meaning behind all of it.

The Holy Anointing Oil blend of Myrrh, Cinnamon, Cane (Biblical Word studies trace this back to Balsam Fir or something similar), and Cassia would have been extremely purifying and cleansing.

What was this oil used ON?

- Tent of Meeting
- Ark of Testimony
- Table & Utensils
- Altar of Incense
- Altar of Burnt Offering — and all utensils, basin, and stand
- Aaron and his sons (the priests)

WHY???

Think through what was happening in this place.

SACRIFICE.

The Lord set aside the Israelites as HIS PEOPLE, but that did not mean that they were forgiven without the presence of blood. And if you do 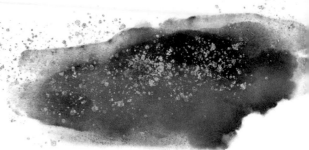 any research into what these sacrificial processes looked like, you'll quickly be shocked by the gruesome and constant presence of blood.

From the start of our fallen relationship with Him, God has demanded sacrifice. It began when Adam and Eve sinned and the Lord clothed them with the skin of an animal in Genesis 3; then we find that pattern continuing through the shedding of blood when creating a covenant with Abram. Sin demands sacrifice. It's an unpleasant but true thought, but even something we may judge as a small error must be covered with blood.

While Moses wanders in the wilderness with the Israelites we see this playing out with extreme specifics as the Lord hands down his design for this sacrifice. Day after day, hour after hour, the priests are shedding blood to cover the sins of their people.

Imagine the smell and the potential for bacteria with all the sacrifices in the temple. It is no coincidence that the Lord commanded them to cover every surface and person in this temple with the specific Anointing Oil blend.

Now we know some of the chemistry and sanitation reasons behind these oils. It is incredible that we have access to these very same oils today. We can actually know exactly what this sacred Anointing Oil that God ordained the priests to use smells like.

Priests were the ones who were chosen to use the Holy Anointing Oil to cleanse and bless the offerings brought into the Tent of Meeting, and later into the temple itself. They would also anoint God's people, and even structures!

Next time you pull out a bottle of oil, try to imagine these priests thousands of years ago doing the same thing!

Exodus II

While not an exact replica of the Holy Anointing oil, the Exodus II™ blend is an amazing way to experience the oils of Exodus.

This blend includes
- Olive Oil
- Myrrh
- Cassia
- Cinnamon
- Calamus
- Black Spruce
- Hyssop
- Vetiver
- Frankincense

With many similar oils found in the Holy Anointing Oil, we love to use this one in our home for fresh breathing air and to support our bodies when they feel stressed in the fall and winter!

In our modern times, we can view the map of the Middle East and chart the possible path of the Israelites. We can imagine where they camped and walked... and quite possibly we may get a little haughty thinking, "How could they have had such a hard time following the Lord -- the Holy Land was so close and it took them forty years?!"

Ummm... yeah. Except in my own heart I disobey and there are times when the Lord lets me wander in my own wilderness because I need to tap into His desires for my life instead of the things I chase on my own.

Have you experienced a time of wandering? Are there any Scriptures that help you pull back into the Lord's desires for your life? Where do you cling during those moments?

What is Anointing?

To "anoint" someone is to cover them with "an ointment." It means "to cover, rub or smear the head or body with oil" and in some cases it means "to pour oil over the head or body." The Hebrew word for anoint, "mashach," is very similar to the English word massage.

The root words for "anoint" in Scripture are:

Hebrew "mashach" -- this verb means "to smear or anoint." This word is used over and over in the Old Testament to talk about anointing the temple and priests.

Greek "Messias" -- this noun means "the anointed one." This word is used in John 1:41 and John 4:25, referring to Jesus (messias is based on the Hebrew word "mashach," the noun version of the above for "anointed").

> "Is anyone among you sick? Let them call the elders of the church to pray over them and anoint them with oil in the name of the Lord"
> James 5:14
>
> "You prepare a table for me in the presence of my enemies. You anoint my head with oil; my cup overflows."
> Psalm 23:5
>
> "It is like precious oil poured on the head, running down the beard, running down on Aaron's beard, down the collar of his robe"
> Psalm 133:2

Note the verse above in Psalm 133 mentions "precious oil." Olive oil wouldn't be referred to as "precious," so we know this was oil of great value being used, oil like our essential oils. Oil poured over Aaron so that it runs down his beard and robe shows the importance and value placed on anointing during that time.

Anointing served many purposes.

- Anointing was performed during a sacred time or to consecrate someone/something for sacred use. We see biblical examples of anointing priests, sacred vessels, kings, and prophets.

- Anointing was done as a part of hospitality. Jews often used oil to refresh their bodies and sometimes offered this service to guests in their home.

- Oil was used for medicinal purposes.

- Bodies of the dead were sometimes anointed. The women who discovered Jesus had been raised from the dead arrived at his tomb with spices and ointments for his body.

Biblical anointing typically involves four things.

- the pouring of oil
- the laying on of hands
- prayer
- blessing

Myrrh (Commiphora myrrha) :: in history

Myrrh is purifying, restorative, revitalizing, and uplifting. It has a thick, rich aroma. Myrrh is an oil high in sesquiterpenes. Sesquiterpenes are a class of compounds that have a direct effect on the hypothalamus, pituitary, and amygdala, the seat of our emotions, making Myrrh a helpful oil for emotional stability and meditation.

Myrrh is a very viscous oil -- it's thick! You'll notice when you open your bottle that it's like a honey, and it will even thicken up over time! For this reason, in ancient times it was often used as a "fixative" or a base for other, more volatile oils. This kept the other oils from evaporating and prolonged the life of the perfumes and ointments. Some ancient references refer to "a Myrrh," using the term much like we would "a lotion" or "an ointment."

Consulting historical records, you will find a variety of recommended uses for Myrrh.

- perfume or medicine
- oral health -- often the resin was chewed as gum!
- an ingredient in healing salves for abrasions and other skin ailments
- bruises, sprains, and aches
- as gum for indigestion, ulcers, colds, coughs, asthma, lung congestion, arthritis pain
- circulatory problems and uterine health
- beauty treatments and skin conditions
- sun protection and insect repellent

Myrrh tip: to keep the oil lid from sticking to the bottle, take a tiny bit of carrier oil and apply along the inside of the threads in the white cap to help it smoothly twist against the glass bottle!

Myrrh :: in scripture

Myrrh is the most commonly-referenced aromatic oil in the Bible. It is the first oil to be mentioned in Genesis 37:25 and the last in Revelation 18:13.

In Genesis 37, we find ten of Jacob's sons dealing with their frustrating and bothersome younger brother, Joseph. This bratty brother had frayed the nerves of his older siblings. In verse 25 they are eating a meal together and discussing their options after throwing their annoying little brother into a "pit" (possibly a well).

"As they sat down to eat their meal, they looked up and saw a caravan of Ishmaelites coming from Gilead. Their camels were loaded with spices, balm and Myrrh, and they were on their way to take them down to Egypt" (Genesis 37:25).

Ahhhhh… Here we see our friend Myrrh make its first appearance.

This is the very first direct mention of an essential oil in Scripture, and it shows up at this pivotal instance in history when Joseph's brothers sell him to spice traders headed to Egypt. This moment serves as a catalyst of change for the whole nation of Israel. His brothers would return to Egypt decades later in a time of famine, bringing gifts of balm and Myrrh to the leader over all of Egypt, their own brother Joseph.

Years earlier Joseph was warned in a dream about an impending famine and has stored ample food supplies for Egypt. This food prompts the starving Israelites to come and eventually they find themselves relocated to Egypt. Generations later they would be slaves to the Egyptians and need a hero to help lead them out of bondage and into freedom (enter: Moses).

Myrrh saw Joseph sold into slavery – the catalyst for the people of God to end up as Egyptian slaves, later to be delivered by God through Moses. We will see its presence in Matthew 2 at the birth of Christ and in Mark 15 at the cross.

Myrrh :: other biblical references

In addition to being a traded item and possibly a commodity of the era (from Genesis 37), here are some of the other mentions of Myrrh in Scripture.

> "All your robes are fragrant with Myrrh and aloes and Cassia;
> from palaces adorned with ivory
> the music of the strings makes you glad."
> Psalm 45:8

- An ingredient in the Holy Anointing oil (Exodus 30:23)
- Part of a 6-month beautification process Esther experienced to prepare for her marriage to the king (Esther 2:12)
- A perfume (Psalm 45:8, Proverbs 7:17, Song of Solomon 1:13, 4:14, 5:13)
- An incense (Song of Solomon 3:6, 4:6)
- An ointment (Song of Solomon 5:5)
- Possibly spices to be eaten (Song of Solomon 5:1)
- A gift for Jesus (and Mary/Joseph) at his birth (Matthew 2:11)
- A mixture with wine, given to those being crucified, present at Christ's death (Mark 15:23)
- Part of the burial preparations for Christ's body (John 19:39)

In Biblical times, Myrrh was a commonly-used oil. We see it scattered all over Scripture, and I've only recently begun noticing the many mentions of plants in Scripture. But now that my eyes are opened... wow! There's so much to learn!

How much more have I missed? How often am I skimming the Bible for what I expect to find, when there are hidden mysteries like the presence of botanicals intermingled within the familiar stories? Consider taking a few minutes to pray that the Lord wakes your mind to these additional ways He speaks!

"When we read of the wise men in Matthew 2:11, Myrrh was among the gifts they offered. Mary would have particularly smiled at the gift of Myrrh knowing that it was also meant for her and not just the babe. She would have known that she could rub it on her abdomen and remove the stretch marks from her pregnancy. She and Joseph would also have known that Myrrh was to be rubbed on the umbilical cord of the newborn child to facilitate healing and prevent infection.

"She would probably have known, as a matter of folk wisdom, that the smell of Myrrh on her body, as she breastfed the Christ Child, would promote a spiritual and emotional feeling of peace and security for both of them. By associating the smell of Myrrh with the security of the mother's breast in infancy would establish an emotional memory that would resurrect these secure feelings any time there was the smell of Myrrh throughout the rest of a person's life.

"The wise men would not have had to explain these things, because such understanding was common knowledge with the peoples of those times."

(Stewart 216)

Cassia (Cinnamomum cassia)

Cassia typically refers to the bark from an evergreen tree originating in southern China. It's very similar to the cinnamon we are familiar with but is quite a bit "hotter" than cinnamon oil. Always use a carrier oil with this one! I usually recommend a new user simply sniff from the bottle at first.

Think of how far this Cassia had to travel to get to the Middle East - this was an expensive oil! Ezekiel 27:19 lists it as a trading commodity along with wine, wrought iron, and calamus.

Historically Cassia has been called an "oil of gladness" for its emotional uplifting effects. It was used to support the immune system and to help the digestive system function smoothly. Cassia has also historically been connected to improving blood circulation.

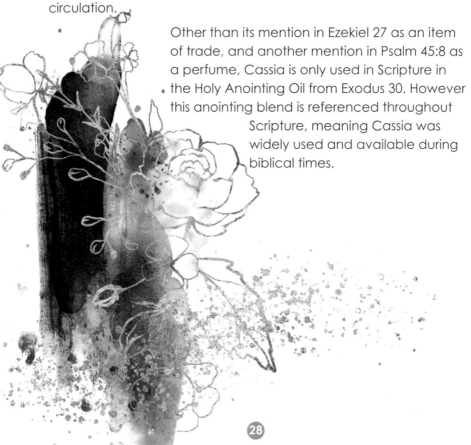

Other than its mention in Ezekiel 27 as an item of trade, and another mention in Psalm 45:8 as a perfume, Cassia is only used in Scripture in the Holy Anointing Oil from Exodus 30. However this anointing blend is referenced throughout Scripture, meaning Cassia was widely used and available during biblical times.

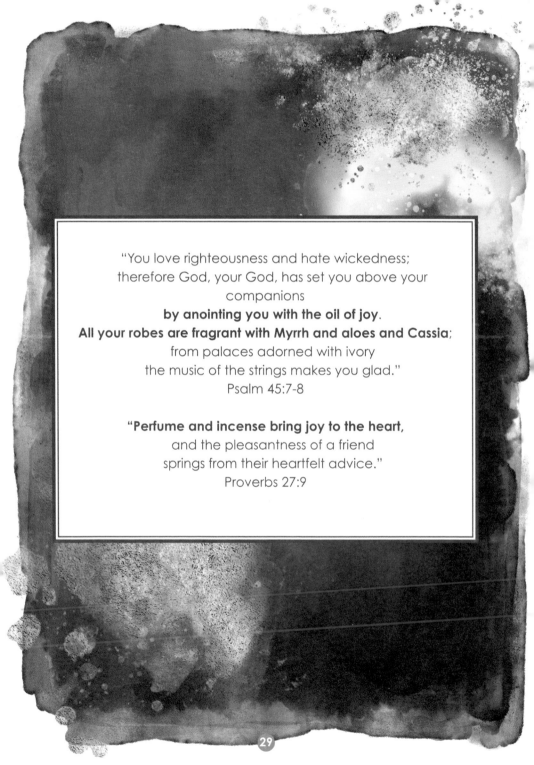

"You love righteousness and hate wickedness;
therefore God, your God, has set you above your
companions
by anointing you with the oil of joy.
All your robes are fragrant with Myrrh and aloes and Cassia;
from palaces adorned with ivory
the music of the strings makes you glad."
Psalm 45:7-8

"Perfume and incense bring joy to the heart,
and the pleasantness of a friend
springs from their heartfelt advice."
Proverbs 27:9

"The Spirit of the Sovereign Lord is on me,
because the Lord has anointed me
to proclaim good news to the poor.
He has sent me to bind up the brokenhearted,
to proclaim freedom for the captives
and release from darkness for the prisoners,
to proclaim the year of the Lord's favor
and the day of vengeance of our God,
to comfort all who mourn,
and provide for those who grieve in Zion—
to bestow on them a crown of beauty
instead of ashes,
the oil of joy
instead of mourning,
and a garment of praise
instead of a spirit of despair.
They will be called oaks of righteousness,
a planting of the Lord
for the display of his splendor."
Isaiah 61:1-3

Onycha (Styrax benzoin)

This obscure oil finds itself on our list of biblical oils because of its mention in the Holy Incense in Exodus 30. That is the only place in Scripture this oil is mentioned. Because of this, historians disagree on the plant to which it refers.

Truly, researching this one baffled me for a bit. Historians have linked the name "Onycha" with two different sources.

The first possible source for Onycha is the *Styrax benzoin* used in the Oils of Ancient Scripture kit (there are some hints it could also be a balsam or laudanum origin, but they are less likely). *Styrax benzoin* is a gum-resin used by ancient Egyptians in the art of perfumery and incense.

The second historical reference to Onycha is when describing the operculum of a snail-like mollusk found in the Red Sea.

Truly, there is no historical record to confirm that the Onycha of the Holy Incense is referring to *Styrax benzoin*, but from my research, it's the only reasonable designation. Mollusks were among the forbidden items God listed out for the Jews in Leviticus 11:9-12, so it's unlikely God would be commanding they ground up the shells and used them in the Holy Incense for the holiest of holy places.

Historically, Onycha (Styrax benzoin) was used for a variety of reasons:

- dental health & care (the resin was even used as dental restorative material!)
- primary ingredient in tinctures for small injuries; used as a disinfectant, local anesthetic, and to speed healing of wounds

As part of the Holy Incense, the fragrance of Onycha wold have perfumed the sanctuary.

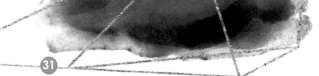

31

Rose of Sharon :: Cistus (Cistus ladanifer)

The Rose of Sharon we read about in Song of Songs is used as a way Solomon's lover describes herself. "I am a rose of Sharon, a lily of the valleys." Solomon answers back, "like a lily among thorns is my darling among the young women" (Song of Songs 2:1-2).

What is this Rose spoken about in Solomon's love letters? The truth is, we aren't quite sure. Because of the time period in history and the roses that might have been in view while writing these love poems together, historians believe it was likely *Cistus ladanifer*, also known as the rock rose.

In the Young Living collection Oils of Ancient Scripture, we find a beautiful gold bottle adorned with the name "Rose of Sharon" but we can also find this same Cistus available as an essential oil outside of the biblical collection.

This beautiful rose has a honey-like scent but is different than the thorny rose we are more familiar with in modern times.

Historically, resin from Cistus was used as an ingredient for incense and used medicinally to treat colds, coughs, menstrual problems, and rheumatism. This resin was commonly found along the shrubs where goats wandered, and the shepherds commonly used it on the skin of their goats to promote healing when injured.

"Sheep can get their head caught in briers and die trying to get untangled. There are horrid little flies that like to torment sheep by laying eggs in their nostrils which turn into worms and drive the sheep to beat their head against a rock, sometimes to death. Their ears and eyes are also susceptible to tormenting insects. So the shepherd anoints their whole head with oil. Then there is peace. That oil forms a barrier of protection against the evil that tries to destroy the sheep.

Do you have times of mental torment? Do the worrisome thoughts invade your mind over and over? Do you beat your head against a wall trying to stop them? Have you ever asked God to anoint your head with oil? He has an endless supply! His oil protects and makes it possible for you to fix your heart, mind, and eyes on Him today and always! There is peace in the valley! May our good good Father anoint your head with oil today so that your cup overflows with blessings! God is good and He is faithful!!"

~Author Unknown

wood (Cedrus atlantica) :: in history

Cedarwood is believed to be the very first essential oil ever distilled. Its history in medicinal and practical uses traces back to the Egyptians and Sumerians, who used Cedarwood in their embalming processes over 5000 years ago. They also used the oil for medicinal purposes and the timber to build dwellings, temples, instruments, coffins, and boats.

The Cedars of Lebanon were magnificent, towering trees which could live as long as 2000 years. It's amazing to think that seedlings around during the life of Jesus might still be rising to the sky in worship today deep in the mountains of Lebanon.

Cedarwood oil today comes from *Cedrus atlantica*, the Cedar species most similar to ancient cedar and much more readily available, as the ancient species is now endangered and protected.

Cedarwood oil contains 98% sesquiterpenes, and inhaling it increases our ability to think clearly. How? Quite simply, sesquiterpenes can cross the blood-brain barrier and oxygenate the brain... simply from sniffing the oil!

I often hear, "Cedarwood helps me sleep at night!" For many people, this is true because it enhances melatonin stimulation in the brain. One of the reasons Cedarwood is often tied to a good night's sleep is because that oxygenation process helps our brains clear the mental clutter. All the things fighting for our attention when we wind down at night can make it hard to settle and rest.

For the same reasons, Cedarwood is an amazing oil to use anytime you need help filtering out the noise and focusing on a task; it's found in many of our most favorite blends like Brain Power™, Highest Potential™, Inspiration™, Into the Future™, GeneYus™, Live with Passion™, Tranquil™, and even StressAway™!

Because Cedarwood clears the brain and improves our ability to think, it is linked to the clearing of many different emotions. Most notably, though, is the connection between Cedarwood and appropriate emotional balance with conceit and pride.

Cedarwood :: in scripture

Cedarwood is mentioned throughout Scripture, often as part of the materials used for building. Let's focus in on one use and learn a little more about this fascinating tree.

Solomon became King following his father David in 971 BC. We can read about his ascension to the throne in 1 Chronicles and 1 Kings. In 1 Kings 3:9 we read of a request he makes of the Lord where he pleads, "give your servant a discerning heart to govern your people and to distinguish between right and wrong. For who is able to govern this great people of yours?"

The Bible records that the Lord was pleased with Solomon's humility in requesting wisdom, the Lord offers him three things:

- a wise and discerning heart "so that there will never have been anyone like you, nor will there ever be " (v12)

- and both wealth and honor "so that in your lifetime you will have no equal among kings" (v13)

- a long life -- "And if you walk in obedience to me and keep my decrees and commands as David your father did, I will give you a long life" (v14)

> "God gave Solomon wisdom and very great insight, and a breadth of understanding as measureless as the sand on the seashore. Solomon's wisdom was greater than the wisdom of all the people of the East, and greater than all the wisdom of Egypt. He was wiser than anyone else, including Ethan the Ezrahite—wiser than Heman, Kalkol and Darda, the sons of Mahol. And his fame spread to all the surrounding nations. He spoke three thousand proverbs and his songs numbered a thousand and five. He spoke about plant life, from the cedar of Lebanon to the hyssop that grows out of walls. He also spoke about animals and birds, reptiles and fish. From all nations people came to listen to Solomon's wisdom, sent by all the kings of the world, who had heard of his wisdom."
>
> 1 Kings 6:11-18

Cedarwood

All this talk about Solomon and no talk about Cedarwood... I know! Hang tight; we're getting there.

So the summary of that story is basically that King Solomon is crazy smart, super famous, and wildly successful. And according to that last passage, he taught people about plants, too!

So take a glance at this passage next because this is where it all begins to unlock.

> "The word of the Lord came to Solomon: 'As for this temple you are building, if you follow my decrees, observe my laws and keep all my commands and obey them, I will fulfill through you the promise I gave to David your father. And I will live among the Israelites and will not abandon my people Israel.'
>
> So Solomon built the temple and completed it. He lined its interior walls with cedar boards, paneling them from the floor of the temple to the ceiling, and covered the floor of the temple with planks of juniper."
>
> 1 Kings 6:11-15

Solomon was endlessly wise. But he was also given some specific directions from the Lord about building the temple, the "house of the Lord." The Lord commands him to line the interior walls with cedar boards - the walls and ceiling.

Have you ever smelled the inside of a Cedar chest? The oil in the wood stays aromatic for years, even a century! Unlike other building materials, when Cedarwood was used to create sturdy buildings, the inhabitants benefited from the Cedar oil for years to come!

So Solomon asks for wisdom. The Lord says, "you be [...] a paraphrase), and then gives him instruction to basic [...] Cedarwood all over everywhere that he's going to live, g[...] and worship.

From our first discussion on Cedarwood, recall that it is high in sesquiterpenes and is highly oxygenating for the brain. This is one of those "aha, Lord... I see what you did there!" kind of moments!

But not only that. Solomon was blessed with more than just wisdom. Because of his humility, the Lord promised him fame and fortune and even a long, long life. In my opinion, all of those things risk the formation of a dictatorial leader with no care for his people, one who is caught up on his own abilities and lacks the humility to consider others.

Unfortunately, later in his reign, Scripture explains that his many wives returned to their idolatrous beliefs. Eventually, 1 Kings 11 records he chased after another god. The Lord speaks sternly to him and lays out the plan for Solomon's demise in 1 Kings 11:9-13.

1 Kings 11:9 says, "The Lord became angry with Solomon because his heart had turned away from the Lord, the God of Israel." Solomon had stopped worshiping the way he should and likely stopped visiting the temple with the regularity of his early reign.

When the Lord instructed Solomon to build the temple, the walls were lined with Cedarwood. That precious cedar oil, which stays in the air for years, was there to support his brain.

But might it also have been a strategic placement from the Lord in other ways? Recall that Cedarwood has an emotional connection to rooting out conceit and pride. This oil is calming and centering and is an ideal oil for a leader to use regularly to encourage humility. The Lord was so kind to have him build the temple out of wood with chemical constituents that work in the hypothalamus to keep one from being prideful.

Divine plan. Incredible.

...mon stopped visiting the temple with ...
...now as he aged he got distracted from ...
...ho had supported him and provided for his ...

...vant to read into this that Cedarwood ...
...olomon from his sinful choices -- Solomon ...
...with God because he lost touch with the oil.

...magine it's similar to the way these things happen with you and me. I get distracted, I find success in something without giving full credit to the Lord -- or I experience a loss and am not able to yield to His sovereignty, and suddenly I'm in a gentle but destructive spiral away from my One True Love. We must choose to keep ourselves yielded to Him.

In a recent Bible Study I came across this pledge. It is recommended we write this out in our own hand, sign at the bottom in commitment, and recommit ourselves to this on a regular basis.

> Having been born into the Kingdom of God, I do hereby acknowledge that God's purchase of my life included all the rights and control of that life for all eternity.
>
> I do further acknowledge that He has not guaranteed me to be free from pain or to have success or prosperity. He has not guaranteed me perfect health. He has not guaranteed me perfect parents. He has not guaranteed me perfect children. He has not guaranteed me the absence of pressures, trials, misunderstandings, or persecution.
>
> What he has promised me is eternal life. What he has promised me is abundant life. What he has promised me is love, joy, peace, patience, gentleness, meekness, and self-control. He has given me all of Himself in exchange for the rights to my life.
>
> Therefore I acknowledge this day the relinquishment of all my rights and expectations, and humbly ask Him by His grace to replace these with a grateful spirit, for whatever in His wisdom He deems to allow for my life.
>
> (modified in DeMoss p146-147)

Cypress *(Cupressus sempervirens)*

Cypress is another oil we find in Scripture used as a building material for large temples and structures. In fact, in the passage we read about the Lord's instructions for Solomon, the NIV translation mentions using Juniper for the floors. Most other translations use the word Cypress here.

Cypress trees were commonplace in biblical times. The Phoenicians and Cretans used Cypress for building ships and houses, the Egyptians often made their sarcophagi from the hard wood, and the Greeks used Cypress to carve statues to their gods.

In Biblical times, Cypress trees were planted in Mediterranean cemeteries, symbolizing that life after death had begun. Cypress trees are still commonly seen at cemeteries around the world.

Emotionally, Cypress supports feelings of security and stability, perfect for the floors of the temple!

Historically, Cypress was known for being supportive of the immune and cardiovascular systems, as well as being rich in monoterpenes. Our ancient friends would have used it for arthritis, laryngitis, scar tissue, and cramps. There are records dating back to 1800 BC mentioning Cypress oil.

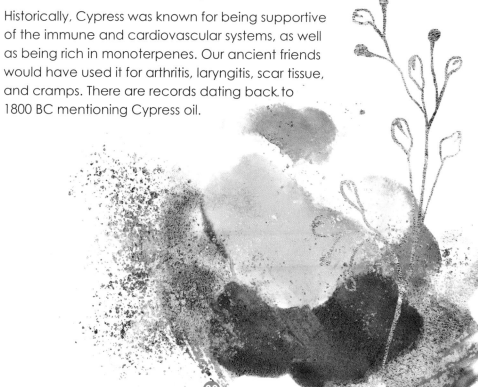

Myrtle (Myrtus communis)

Myrtle has a bright, refreshing scent. When you take a deep breath, you'll feel your lungs smile just like they do when you smell eucalyptus!

Myrtle is a flowering evergreen bush that can grow to be quite large. It's native to southern Europe, north Africa, western Asia, Micronesia, and the Indian Subcontinent.

Historically, it was primarily used in religious ceremonies for purification rituals. Our ancient friends would have loved to know it is incredibly supportive of their endocrine system, specifically the thyroid, and is very soothing to the respiratory system.

There are two fascinating ways that Myrtle shows up in Scripture.

First, Myrtle is part of Sukkot -- the Feast of Tabernacles. Historically the Feast of Tabernacles celebrates the end of the Exodus (the 40 years of wandering the Israelites experienced between Egypt and the Promised Land).

In Jewish liturgy and the Feast of Tabernacles, there are four sacred plants used during Sukkot to represent the different types of personalities making up the community. Those species are lulav (palm branch), hadas (myrtle), aravah (willow), and etrog (citron). On the next page, you can read about the significance of the plants and their meaning in creating a culture of joy and cohesion.

In this ceremony, Myrtle has a pleasing fragrance but lacks a pleasant taste; this represents those community members known for good deeds yet lack that would come from studying

In the Bible no attempt is made to explain the symbolism of the four species. They probably symbolized the fertility of the land as evidenced in the harvest just concluded, and as desired for the coming season, especially with a view to the fact that the rains are due immediately after Sukkot. The Midrash gives a number of moral and homiletic interpretations (see Lev. R. 30:9–12); the most popular (ibid., 30:12) is based on the qualities of the four trees. The etrog has both "taste and odor," the date (palm) only taste, the Myrtle only odor, the willow none. "Taste and odor" symbolize "Torah and good works"; respectively the four species represent four categories of Jews insofar as they possess both, one, or none of these virtues. But Israel is regarded as a whole, and the failings of one are compensated for by the virtues of the others.

("Four Species")

Esther

The second place Myrtle shows up in Scripture as a fascinating study topic is in the book of Esther.

In Hebrew, the word for Myrtle is the feminine form of the word "hadas," Hadassah. Hadassah is Esther's Jewish name.

The Book of Esther tells the story of a Jewish heroine who saved her people from annihilation during the reign of King Xerxes I (Ahasuerus) of Persia, who ruled from 486 to 465 BC.

After the disturbing dismissal of his first wife, Xerxes issues a decree that all the beautiful young women should be brought to his castle for him to choose a new wife. Our friend Esther had been raised by her kind older uncle, Mordecai. He wisely guides her through the process of meeting the king and advises her.

Prior to meeting the King, Esther and the other girls would go through extensive ritual beauty treatments. "Before a young woman's turn came to go in to King Xerxes, she had to complete twelve months of beauty treatments prescribed for the women, six months with oil of Myrrh and six with perfumes and cosmetics" (Esther 2:12).

Knowing how wonderful Myrrh is for the skin, it makes me smile to think about six full months with oil of Myrrh. Yes, please!

Esther wins the favor of Xerxes and becomes his Queen, yet their relationship is still one of great submission; she can only enter his presence when he has called for her or risk death. When Mordecai learns the plan of a king's advisor to destroy the Jews in Persia, he insists Esther break protocol and enter the king's presence uncalled. She declines.

> When Esther's words were reported to Mordecai, he sent back this answer: "Do not think that because you are in the king's house you alone of all the Jews will escape. For if you remain silent at this time, relief and deliverance for the Jews will arise from another place, but you and your father's family will perish. And who knows but that you have come to your royal position for such a time as this?"
> Esther 4:12-14

Esther's response is to have the Jews fast for her. She goes before the king and steps into the hard place, takes a chance, and her willing participation provides a way for the Jews to be rescued. The Lord used this gentle, obedient woman to save His People.

In this she proves to be unlike the Myrtle plant's description.

Where the plant has a pleasant smell and unpleasant taste, representing good deeds and a lack of knowledge, Esther shows she is balanced. She has knowledge, and she walks it out in hard times. What a beautiful Myrtle example.

Ah. "For such a time as this." That is a phrase I've heard often when facing a difficult situation or helping a friend in one. So often we come across a hard spot in life and realize that all the ways we were learning and leaning on Him in the past have prepared us "for such a time as this."

Our family recently went through a hard season and as we were coming back out of it and finally feeling "normal," a close friend asked me what verses of Scripture had been encouraging or helpful to me personally to make it through. I thought about it for a while and answered her. "None specifically. I feel like I've been through a long season of trusting the Lord."

What I mean is, years before facing these recent deep, soul-searching valleys, I set a secure foundation in simply trusting the Lord and studying His Word -- in the good days, in the bad days, in the struggles, and in the praises. So when a season of true heartache came on our family, I didn't have to search for a verse to give me comfort and put it on sticky notes all over my house as a reminder (though that's a good trick, too!).

Like it says in Psalm 119:11, "I have hidden your word in my heart that I might not sin against you." The choice to hide the Word in my heart gave me tools and confidence to trust the Lord when nothing around me made sense.

When people quote Christian platitudes like "the Lord never gives you more than you can handle!," I know to refute them. That's just not true. Scripture does say in 1 Corinthians 10:13 that we won't be tempted beyond what we can handle.

But as for hardships? Oh yes. He often does give us more than we can handle. How else will we learn to lean on Him?

The call of Christ is not "believe in me so you can power through your life on your own strength!" but rather "Trust in the Lord with all your heart and lean not on your own understanding" (Psalm 3:5).

I'm so thankful that He knows about the hard stuff and has sent His Comforter (the Holy Spirit) to comfort me. He knows the relational hurts, the wounds of the Enemy, the grief we will face. He knows it all, and He is here. Set your foundation on Him in the good times so you will be prepared for the valley.

Frankincense (Boswellia carterii) :: in history

Frankincense and Myrrh are the two most commonly mentioned oils in Scripture simply because they were two of the most commonly used oils during that time period.

This is my personal go-to oil for everything from physical to emotional support. It's our "stranded on a deserted island and you can only have one" oil. When in doubt, get the Frankincense out.

Our ancient friends felt the same way!

Frankincense starts as a resin extracted from the Boswellia tree. As with other common medicinal plants like Eucalyptus and Melaleuca, there are many varieties. Depending on the momentary need, you may prefer one species over another.

The grade (or quality) of Frankincense is determined by the method and timing of harvest, as well as the techniques used to "tap" the trees without destroying the tree itself. This is a very complex and specific process, and in some parts of the world the trees are managed by families who can trace their genealogy and land management back to biblical times.

Historically, Frankincense, also known as olibanum or lebonah, was harvested as a dry resin and steam distilled to create an oil for perfumes and used in skincare. Ancient Chinese medicine recommends the use of Frankincense and Myrrh for antibacterial and "blood moving" uses. In Egypt, it was used to cleanse bodies before mummification.

Frankincense is high in monoterpenes, which help eliminate toxins in the body. It is commonly used in meditation and spiritual practices, and the resin can be found burning as incense in many beautiful cathedrals and houses of worship.

Frankincense was also used to anoint newborn sons of kings and priests. It was is an oil of great value.

Frankincense :: in scripture

Probably the most familiar mention of Frankincense in Scripture is when we read in Matthew 2 about it being given to Mary and Joseph at the birth of Jesus.

But by this point in the New Testament, Frankincense has been mentioned several dozen times directly or indirectly (as a member of another combination such as the Holy Incense of Exodus 30).

The Holy Incense was part of the temple traditions and served other purposes as well. In Numbers 16, we read of a plague the Lord sends to destroy the Israelites, but Aaron fills his censer with the Holy Incense and steps between the living and those already dead from the plague; he raises the burning censer and makes atonement for them.

Isaiah 60 prophesies the arrival of Jesus through the use of beautiful imagery and foretells His impact on Earth.

> Nations will come to your light,
>   and kings to the brightness of your dawn.
> ...And all from Sheba will come,
>   bearing gold and incense
>   and proclaiming the praise of the Lord.
> Isaiah 60:3, 6b

The "Incense" mentioned alongside gold in verse 6 refers to the Holy Incense, which contained Myrrh and Frankincense.

> "On coming to the house, they saw the child with his mother Mary, and they bowed down and worshiped him. Then they opened their treasures and presented him with gifts of gold, Frankincense and Myrrh."
> Matthew 2:11

Gold, Frankincense, and Myrrh as gifts for the newborn Christ child. Gifts for health. Gifts for royalty.

"For I have come down from heaven not to do my will but to do the will of him who sent me." (John 6:38)

Jesus comes from Heaven to the earth; He leaves the streets of gold for our dusty roads. The gift of gold would provide financial options for Mary & Joseph. Along with their gifts, the Magi brought news that Herod was looking for the babe. Soon after, Herod would give orders to kill all boys around Bethlehem aged two years old and under. This gold allowed them to safely escape to Egypt. Symbolically, I feel the gold is also a reminder of the heavenly roads he walked before descending into our realm.

As for the Frankincense and Myrrh brought by the Magi, these are reminiscent of the Holy Incense. I like to think the fragrance of Heaven will smell something like that beautiful blend.

Gold streets and the aroma of Holy Incense. Isn't it a striking image that the Magi brought Jesus gifts that would be familiar to his eyes and nose?

Obviously, Mary and Joseph knew the Frankincense would be helpful to them as well. Just like we mentioned the Myrrh being great for stretch marks and the umbilical cord, Frankincense would have been used to support the new mother's healing skin. The emotional impact of Frankincense oil, most noted for help releasing negative emotions and responding to grief and loss, would have been helpful as they headed into Egypt.

The next few years for Mary and Joseph would be challenging and scary. Jesus birth brought them into the Biblical narrative and theirs would not be an easy life.

But, OH, what wonder we find when we see the trials in our life as an opportunity for God to show up. When our gratitude in a painful moment allows us to see past the discomfort and put our eyes on our true Hope.

"Mary treasured up all these things and pondered them in her heart" (Luke 2:19).

Indeed, Mary, I pray we all learn to observe and treasure the special moments the way you did.

Frankincense and the Mystery

Over and over in the New Testament, Paul writes about "this mystery, which is Christ in you" (1 Colossians 1:27).

We read about this mystery in Colossians chapters 1 and 4, First Corinthians chapters 2 and 15, and Ephesians chapters 1, 3, 5, and 6, as well as in several other letters.

It is well described in 1 Timothy 3:16:

> "the mystery from which true godliness springs is great:
> He appeared in the flesh,
>   was vindicated by the Spirit,
> was seen by angels,
>   was preached among the nations,
> was believed on in the world,
>   was taken up in glory."

The mystery is Christ. He came from heaven to us -- royalty choosing to live with the peasants. He gave up all the strappings of being God and became man. John 1:14 says simply, "The Word became flesh."

Why was this necessary?

> "For surely it is not angels he helps, but Abraham's descendants. For this reason he had to be made like them, fully human in every way, in order that he might become a merciful and faithful high priest in service to God, and that he might make atonement for the sins of the people. Because he himself suffered when he was tempted, he is able to help those who are being tempted."
> Hebrews 2:16-18

From the moment of Adam's sin in the beginning, in Genesis 3, God makes it clear that the only way we achieve a right relationship with Him is through the covering of blood. Verse 21 says God made garments to cover Adam and Eve's nakedness, killing an animal to cover their sin.

In Leviticus 5, the sin offering is explained to the Israelites, outlining the perfect animals required as sacrifices. Among other specific requirements, the blood was to be poured out at the base of the altar. "In this way the priest will make atonement for them for the sin they have committed, and they will be forgiven" (Leviticus 5:3).

Old Testament law is complex, difficult, and impossible to follow perfectly. The law of the Old Testament serves as a reflection back to Christ. The law exposes our inability to follow it completely, and thus reflects our inconsistencies, untruths, and misdemeanors fully onto the only One who can follow that law.

Jesus was the unblemished Lamb for sacrifice. He is the only man to have walked this earth who followed the law perfectly. Where I trip, He skips. Where I stumble, He glides. And when I fall, it is His hand extended so that I may rise. He is the High Priest making the ultimate sacrifice.

What does this have to do with Frankincense? Ahhhh, there's the beauty. And the revelation of the mystery.

Frankincense and Myrrh were both gathered as resin from trees. The method for retrieving the resin is fascinating. Frankincense is harvested by wounding the tree in a process called "tapping." Harvesters well-trained in this practice will slit the tree so that the sap runs. This sap, much like the tree's blood, runs to the surface to heal the wound. The resin hardens on the surface of the tree.

So think this through. Only after the tree is wounded and bleeding does it create the life-giving resin long sought after. That is the very picture of a perfect Christ that bled and died on a tree.

That blood is a covering for our sins and transgressions. We can never live perfectly; we will not meet that standard. The standard is perfection. Because God knew we couldn't do it, He sent His Son.

"for all have sinned and fall short of the glory of God, and all are justified freely by his grace through the redemption that came by Christ Jesus. God presented Christ as a sacrifice of atonement, through the shedding of his blood—to be received by faith." Romans 3:23-25

How blessed is God! And what a blessing he is! He's the Father of our Master, Jesus Christ, and takes us to the high places of blessing in him. Long before he laid down earth's foundations, he had us in mind, had settled on us as the focus of his love, to be made whole and holy by his love. Long, long ago he decided to adopt us into his family through Jesus Christ. (What pleasure he took in planning this!) He wanted us to enter into the celebration of his lavish gift-giving by the hand of his beloved Son.

Because of the sacrifice of the Messiah, his blood poured out on the altar of the Cross, we're a free people—free of penalties and punishments chalked up by all our misdeeds. And not just barely free, either. Abundantly free! He thought of everything, provided for everything we could possibly need, letting us in on the plans he took such delight in making. He set it all out before us in Christ, a long-range plan in which everything would be brought together and summed up in him, everything in deepest heaven, everything on planet earth.

It's in Christ that we find out who we are and what we are living for. Long before we first heard of Christ and got our hopes up, he had his eye on us, had designs on us for glorious living, part of the overall purpose he is working out in everything and everyone.

It's in Christ that you, once you heard the truth and believed it (this Message of your salvation), found yourselves home free— signed, sealed, and delivered by the Holy Spirit. This signet from God is the first installment on what's coming, a reminder that we'll get everything God has planned for us, a praising and glorious life.

The Message, Ephesians 1:3-14

Friend, if you have never reached out to the Lord
His forgiveness, do so today. We can try so hard t
and be better and better, yet at the end of the d
still true: "for all have sinned and fall short of the g

But "If you declare with your mouth, "Jesus is Lord
your heart that God raised him from the dead, y
(Romans 10:9).

The following prayer can be found in many church books or
prayer. I encourage you to take a quiet moment and seek the
Lord. Seek and pray. And turn your life over to Him.

Merciful God,
we confess that we have sinned against you
in thought, word, and deed,
by what we have done,
and by what we have left undone.

We have not loved you
with our whole heart and soul
and mind and strength.

We have not loved our neighbors as ourselves.

In your mercy,
forgive what we have been,
help us amend what we are,
and direct what we shall be,
so that we may delight in your will
and walk in your ways,
to the glory of your holy name.

Let the Lord meet you in this moment. His arms
are a place of rest and He aches to take your
burdens. "Come to me, all you who are weary
and burdened, and I will give you rest. Take
my yoke upon you and learn from me, for I
am gentle and humble in heart, and you
will find rest for your souls. For my
yoke is easy and my burden is
light." Matthew 11:28-30

(Hyssopus officinalis)

Hyssop is a brightly-colored shrub that resembles lavender in some ways, though the blooms can be blue, pink, or white. Both Hyssop and Lavender are from the mint family of flowering plants, called Lamiaceae.

Historically, leaves of Hyssop were used to make a strong tea to help with nose, throat, and lung afflictions. The oil was also applied to bruises.

In Scripture we find the primary use of Hyssop was for ritual cleansing and ceremonial offerings. In Leviticus 13 we find instructions for a ritual cleansing of lepers involving Cedarwood and Hyssop; in the next chapter, we read about Hyssop used in more complicated recipes for skin diseases and mold remediation.

Recall back to when we discussed Myrrh. In Genesis 37 we read about Joseph's brothers selling him to the Myrrh traders and how his journey to Egypt resulted in the Nation of Israel relocating to Egypt. Over 400 years after that, the Israelites were still in Egypt serving as slaves to the Egyptians. In Exodus 5, Moses begins negotiating with Pharaoh to "Let my people go!" Pharaoh refuses and the Egyptians are subjected to 10 plagues sent by God against the people. The 10th plague is on the firstborn.

To protect themselves, the Lord said to Moses and Aaron that the people should take a perfect lamb and slaughter it. In Exodus 12 the Israelites are instructed to paint their door posts with the blood from this lamb, using Hyssop branches. They are to dip the Hyssop branch into the blood and "put some of the blood on the top and on both sides of the door frame." Some translations say to "strike the lintel and the two side posts."

Every firstborn son in Egypt would die -- Egyptians and Israelites -- but those who were in their homes, "under the blood of the lamb," would be spared. They would be "passed over" by the angel of death. This is where we get the traditional Passover feast.

By striking the door in this pattern with the hyssop and the blood, they made a CROSS pattern on the door with the red blood, and the Hyssop leaves would be bruised as they struck the doors, releasing the scent of the oil. The Israelites would have smelled the blood intermingled with the crisp scent of Hyssop as they protected their homes.

The Old Testament ritual of Passover foreshadows Christ's crucifixion, where we read about Hyssop once again. He is the New Testament Passover Lamb.

Significance of the Passover Lamb Then and Now

1. A lamb must die. "Every man shall take a lamb according to their fathers' houses, a lamb for a household" (Exodus 12:1). A lamb would die during the passover, and Jesus is the Lamb who died on the cross.

2. The instructions were clear. Exodus 12 is a detailed chapter that provides specific instructions for the Israelites. From the perfection of the lamb to the size of the household, the instructions are very clear. They are even given specific wording to use with their families when they recount the Passover story. The New Testament provides clear instructions for us to be saved, as well. "If you declare with your mouth, "Jesus is Lord," and believe in your heart that God raised him from the dead, you will be saved" (Romans 10:9).

3. They are to eat the lamb. Exodus 12:8 details how to eat the lamb, with unleavened bread and bitter herbs. Likewise, we are to consume the Word daily; we should be full of the knowledge of Him.

4. Share the lamb. Exodus 12:4 explains that the lamb is for everyone. We know there is always room at the table of Grace and we are called to share the Lamb with all. Because God loved the whole world, He gave us His Son (John 3:16-17).

While Christ's death wouldn't be the end of His story here on Earth, it was necessary for the perfect Lamb to die in order for His Blood to cover our sins. Jesus came to earth knowing He would die in one of the most gruesome and torturous forms of execution.

It was customary to offer those being crucified a cheap Roman wine mixed with Myrrh as a painkiller to help dull the senses and deal with the horrors of their death. Jesus refused it when first offered at the start, but just before His death, He accepted one final drink. . .

"Later, knowing that everything had now been finished, and so that Scripture would be fulfilled, Jesus said, "I am thirsty." A jar of wine vinegar was there, so they soaked a sponge in it, put the sponge on a stalk of the hyssop plant, and lifted it to Jesus' lips. When he had received the drink, Jesus said, "It is finished." With that, he bowed his head and gave up his spirit."

John 19:28-30

If you read the passage on crucifixion in full and in several gospels, you'll see that Jesus was offered two kinds of wine. The first wine was mixed with gall, which Christ refused once He tasted it. The one He later accepted was wine mixed with Myrrh.

The wine was lifted up on a stalk of hyssop. It is believed that the use of hyssop at crucifixions may have helped in some small way to ease the suffering of those being crucified, as it is extremely soothing to the lungs when inhaled. Victims of crucifixion die from suffocation, due to the weight of their own bodies pulling down on them and their lungs filling with fluid. Hyssop is supportive to the respiratory system and helps break up nasal fluid.

As the branch was lifted to his face, I have no doubt the aroma of hyssop mixed with blood was strikingly similar to the aroma the Israelites smelled as they prepared for the Passover.

When you use Hyssop oil in your home, I encourage you to remember you are inhaling the very same aroma our Savior experienced as He gave His life as a ransom for our sins.

No rooster crow was needed the morning after the Passover to wake from slumber. Egypt woke to the rising sound of mothers screaming as they found the bodies of their dead firstborn.

Pharaoh, who had also lost his first born, would be calling for Moses and Aaron within a few hours. He begged the Israelites to leave quickly.

Generations earlier, God cut covenant with Abram (later to be renamed Abraham). He foretold of the Israelites under Egyptian slavery and their eventual rescue. "I will punish the nation they serve as slaves, and afterward they will come out with great possessions" (Genesis 15:14).

"The Israelites did as Moses instructed and asked the Egyptians for articles of silver and gold and for clothing. The Lord had made the Egyptians favorably disposed toward the people, and they gave them what they asked for; so they plundered the Egyptians" (Exodus 12:33, 35-36).

Recall that we studied the Ebers Papyrus having origins in Egypt around this time. Egyptians loved their oils and recipes. It's easy to imagine they would have considered oils as something in their possession to be plundered by the Israelites.

The Israelites would wander for 40 years in the desert. While I'm sure they interacted with many traders along the way, the recipes given to them in the Holy Anointing Oil and Holy Incense would have been comprised of ingredients God knew they already had in their possession or could easily get.

I believe the "great possessions" from Genesis 15:14 would certainly have included precious oils they would use to worship Him as they journeyed toward the Promised Land.

Aloes :: Sandalwood (Santalum album)

Sandalwood is the most valuable tree in the world. The central part of the tree -- the heartwood -- is used in the distillation process to create the deeply aromatic oil. The Sandalwood tree is considered a "parasitic" tree which taps the roots of other species for water and inorganic nutrients. Each sapling usually thrives between several host trees. The oil quality from a Sandalwood tree is best in an older tree near the end of its life.

Historically, Sandalwood was used for meditation and embalming. It was common for Pharaohs of ancient Egypt to be buried with alabaster jars of perfumes including Sandalwood.

Oil from the Sandalwood tree was a treasured aromatic! Sandalwood is high in sesquiterpenes and is oxygenating for the brain, helping with clear thinking and focus.

Today we also find that it's commonly used for skincare and is a favorite at bedtime to encourage good sleep.

Sandalwood is in many skincare products as well as treasured oil blends like Acceptance™, Awaken™, Build Your Dream™, Dream Catcher™, Forgiveness™, Gathering, Harmony™, Highest Potential™, Inner Child™, Inspiration™ -- that's an alphabetical listing and I could keep going! This one is so beneficial for us!

In Scripture we read of a plant called "aloes." This is not the "aloe" that we think of in terms of a cactus with a gooey liquid to soothe our wounds (though that one is pretty awesome, too!). Rather, this early aloewood is likely to be what we now call Sandalwood.

Sandalwood was mentioned in Psalm 45:8 as a perfume, along with Myrrh and Cassia. This combination was mentioned again in Proverbs 7:17. Anyone else thinking the combination of these three must be a beautiful aroma? I'm trying it for sure!

In John 19 we read of Sandalwood (aloes) used by Joseph & Nicodemus when preserving Jesus's body.

"Joseph of Arimathea asked Pilate for the body of Jesus. Now Joseph was a disciple of Jesus, but secretly because he feared the Jewish leaders. With Pilate's permission, he came and took the body away. He was accompanied by Nicodemus, the man who earlier had visited Jesus at night. Nicodemus brought a mixture of Myrrh and aloes, about seventy-five pounds. Taking Jesus' body, the two of them wrapped it, with the spices, in strips of linen. This was in accordance with Jewish burial customs. At the place where Jesus was crucified, there was a garden, and in the garden a new tomb, in which no one had ever been laid. Because it was the Jewish day of Preparation and since the tomb was nearby, they laid Jesus there."

John 19:38-42

Joseph of Arimathea was an extremely wealthy and prominent man within the Jewish community who had secretly become a follower of Jesus. He risked a LOT in requesting Jesus' body and placing it within his own tomb.

The mixture of Myrrh and Sandalwood he used would have been extremely costly! Nicodemus brought a volume of oil equal to around $150,000-200,000 in today's dollars!

Joseph and Nicodemus understood the enormity of what Jesus had done and were willing to give up everything to honor the sacrifice.

"Who believes what we've heard and seen?
Who would have thought God's saving power would look
like this?

The servant grew up before God—a scrawny seedling,
a scrubby plant in a parched field.
There was nothing attractive about him,
nothing to cause us to take a second look.
He was looked down on and passed over,
a man who suffered, who knew pain firsthand.
One look at him and people turned away.
We looked down on him, thought he was scum.
But the fact is, it was our pains he carried—
our disfigurements, all the things wrong with us.
We thought he brought it on himself,
that God was punishing him for his own failures.
But it was our sins that did that to him,
that ripped and tore and crushed him—our sins!

He took the punishment, and that made us whole.
Through his bruises we get healed.
We're all like sheep who've wandered off and gotten lost.
We've all done our own thing, gone our own way.
And God has piled all our sins, everything we've done wrong,
on him, on him.

He was beaten, he was tortured,
but he didn't say a word.
Like a lamb taken to be slaughtered
and like a sheep being sheared,
he took it all in silence.

Justice miscarried, and he was led off—
and did anyone really know what was happening?
He died without a thought for his own welfare,
beaten bloody for the sins of my people.
They buried him with the wicked,
threw him in a grave with a rich man,
Even though he'd never hurt a soul
or said one word that wasn't true.

Still, it's what God had in mind all along,
to crush him with pain.
The plan was that he give himself as an offering for sin
so that he'd see life come from it—life, life, and more life.
And God's plan will deeply prosper through him.

Out of that terrible travail of soul,
he'll see that it's worth it and be glad he did it.
Through what he experienced, my righteous one, my servant,
will make many "righteous ones,"
as he himself carries the burden of their sins.
Therefore I'll reward him extravagantly—
the best of everything, the highest honors—
Because he looked death in the face and didn't flinch,
because he embraced the company of the lowest.
He took on his own shoulders the sin of the many,
he took up the cause of all the black sheep."

The Message, Isaiah 53

In Closing...

I pray that this study of our plants and oils in Biblical history has helped to show you how God's Words are still active. The message is alive and relevant for us today.

One of the saddest things I hear a Christan say is, "I don't read the Old Testament, I stay mostly in the New."

Friend. I pray that you will seek the Lord. Ask Him for wisdom. And open the Old Testament to more than just the familiar Psalms and encouraging Proverbs.

The Bible is full of real people just like you and me. Yes, they lived during a different time. But they struggled just like we do! They celebrated their achievements, sought God, and wandered from Him. The Lord uses those stories to show us who He is.

When you read your Bible, try reading it with this request in your mind, "Lord, show me how Jesus is better."

Adam was created in the image of God. Jesus IS God. Adam is the lesser Jesus. He was the first man, made perfect, but he sinned and brought death for us all. Jesus was born perfect man and lived a sinless life.

When we read about the Patriarchs (those are the scriptural "founding fathers" from Genesis -- Abraham, Jacob, etc), we must understand the purpose they serve. They were extolled for their faith, but they were imperfect men. Only Jesus is the true foundation of our faith.

Moses was used by God to rescue the Israelites from their bondage in Egypt. Oh, but Jesus is the better Moses. Jesus has rescued us from the ultimate bondage and slavery of sin through His death and resurrection.

The detailed sacrifices, anointing rules, and tabernacle worship are but a pale shadow of the One who showed us the better and perfect way when He gave His Blood for us.

We briefly studied how Esther stepped into her "such a time as this" moment to courageously beg the King when the Israelites were threatened with destruction. Jesus is the better Esther. He didn't just speak to the Father about our rescue, He put Himself in our place on the Cross and took the wrath on our behalf.

King Solomon and his wisdom pale in comparison to Christ Jesus and the wisdom He showed during his life on earth.

Every person and every story told in the Bible serves the purpose of pointing us toward God and His Glory.

The earth is full of the glory of the Lord.

Make no mistake, these plants we have studied are NOT the glory, but rather they reflect to us the goodness and great plan of our God. They show us His Glory. They serve as a reminder of the One who is the ultimate Healer and Great Physician.

The Old and New Testaments are full of opportunities for us to see how Jesus is better. Jesus is the fulfillment of scripture. He is the fulfillment of the promises.

In Luke 24 we find a passage often called "the Road to Emmaus," which takes place after the resurrection. Here, Jesus walks unrecognized with a few men on their way to the village of Emmaus. They discuss whether Jesus of Nazareth is really who they hoped He would be. Jesus calls them foolish and then verse 27 says "And beginning with Moses and all the Prophets, he explained to them what was said in all the Scriptures concerning himself."

Imagine how His voice must have delighted with joy at the retelling of that beautiful history and the countless ways it pointed to His life on earth! Oh, how I can't wait for the day when I can sit in heaven at His feet and hear Him explain every Old Testament word in detail. I'm praying we can even pop in some DVDs and watch the stories come to life on a screen!

Friend, let God speak to you through his living Word! Both Testaments point to the redemptive story of Christ! Ask Him to help you understand... And open that Bible!

"For the word of God is alive and active. Sharper than any double-edged sword, it penetrates even to dividing soul and spirit, joints and marrow; it judges the thoughts and attitudes of the heart."

Hebrews 4:12

Now What?

Oh friend, I pray this has been an exciting chance to dive into scripture together. I trust you have learned at least one new thing with me on this adventure!

I also pray that your love for the Word of God has been reignited and that you will search ever closer through the pages of Scripture for the beautiful side-notes He gives us through nature's appearance in the narrative.

I believe that we have been given a calling to go forth and anoint and pray for one another. When we realize that these amazing wellness tools have been given to us to share with others, it is with joy and excitement that we can go forth to bless.

We have natural options and tools for our wellness.

We have a Savior who loves us and who gave His life as a perfect ransom for our sins.

We must tell others!

Share Christ and His Truth with those around you. If that does not come naturally to you, use the oils as a conversation starter. Speak to those within your circle of influence and teach them how to care for their families and loved ones with God's natural tools. Pray that this opens doors for you to talk to them about the Great Physician.

Thank you for trusting me on this journey of knowledge. It is always a humbling privilege to share what I've learned, especially when it has to do with the Word of God and the options He has given us to heal and care for our families.

Blessings to you and yours.

xoxo, Erin

PS - I would be honored to hear from you! Please feel free to reach out using the contact information on the following pages!

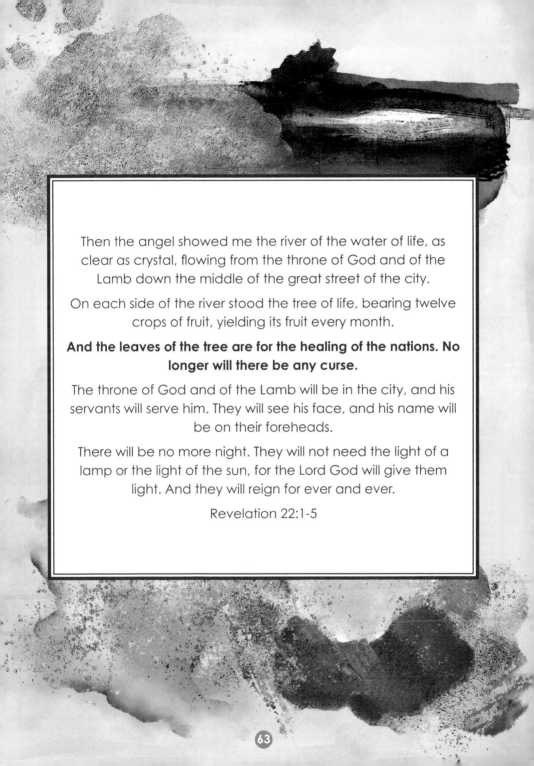

Then the angel showed me the river of the water of life, as clear as crystal, flowing from the throne of God and of the Lamb down the middle of the great street of the city.

On each side of the river stood the tree of life, bearing twelve crops of fruit, yielding its fruit every month.

And the leaves of the tree are for the healing of the nations. No longer will there be any curse.

The throne of God and of the Lamb will be in the city, and his servants will serve him. They will see his face, and his name will be on their foreheads.

There will be no more night. They will not need the light of a lamp or the light of the sun, for the Lord God will give them light. And they will reign for ever and ever.

Revelation 22:1-5

Teaching a Class

Teaching a class on the Biblical Oils is so easy! Don't be intimidated!

With this book and your Bible, you can totally do it!

Structuring a class is very simple and I would be delighted to give you a few tips and the flow for your event.

Prepare before class. Grab this book, your Bible, and the Oils of Ancient Scripture Collection! Invite your friends and family to join you in your living room so you can share the story with them!

Determine ahead of time if you will provide light snacks or beverages for your friends.

Suggested Class Agenda

01. I like to pray before starting class. It's a good chance to slow down, honor the Lord who has allowed you to teach, ask Him to help you teach with wisdom, and set the tone for the content.

02. Introduce Yourself. Take a few minutes to tell your "oily" story. I always start with my story (how I got started using oils, and why this class content is something I want to teach) and let it go from there. This helps "authenticate" you to anyone who doesn't already know you.

If you're teaching for a group who doesn't know you at all - like at a church or in a friend's home - have a member of that group introduce you to build your credibility with your audience.

03. Quite simply, work your way through the book. Don't just read it, though! Explain it to your friends. Elaborate and tell your own stories. Add in any additional research you've done.

It may be helpful for you to jot down an outline for your class on a piece of paper referencing the page numbers in this book and the scripture references you're using, as well as any additional content you want to cover or read. This helps keep me on track and lessens the chance I overlook something I really wanted to teach.

04. When you get to a scripture passage, have someone else read it. You may need to ask your friends to bring their bibles to class so they're not scrolling their bible app while you're teaching!

05. As you get to each oil of scripture, pass around the oil! Take a deep huff yourself before you let that precious bottle go!

I usually suggest that my audience take a drop of oil if they desire, but with Cassia I do suggest they just take a light sniff of the bottle since it's a hot oil. I also keep carrier oil on hand at class just in case someone has a reaction to an oil.

06. As you learn more by diving into Scripture, I encourage you to enhance your class with additional information. Your friends will be so excited to hear YOUR take on these oils and what God has taught YOU about them. Trust me. As much as I may think this book is an awesome starting point for a class, your friends would rather hear YOU and just have you read from a book.

07. Close the class. Some people like to present a "purchase" opportunity at the end of the class. I always have a close at the end of a class ("here's how you can get your own oils!") but I prefer not to make this class "salesy" at all. How you handle that is completely up to you!

Consider having a list of future classes available for your attendees. This lets them know you're an ongoing resource for oils and oil education.

Finally, friends do not doubt your ability to be a good teacher. I believe if you truly intend to let the Lord speak through you, He will do that!

I can't wait to hear of your successes teaching your friends!

Hey guys! This is my family right here! I'm a Jesus-loving, essential oil-using, mama -- and I love these three people fiercely! Bronce and I have been married for 15+ years, and together we lead a team of over 30,000 Young Living Essential Oil families called the JoyDroppers. We are focused on education and leadership for our tribe. I pray they can see how deeply I love them and want them to know Jesus like I do. It is an honor to serve each one.

keep in Touch!

ErinRodgers.com
theJoyDroppers.com
Erin@theJoyDroppers.com
Facebook.com/erinrodgers
Instagram.com/heyerinrodgers

Oils of Ancient Scripture

The ten oils upon which this book focuses can be found in a collection from Young Living Essential oils. The Oils of Ancient Scripture is the best way to get all ten oils - and the only current way to get some biblical favorites such as Myrtle, Onycha, and Cassia which have limited availability.

Oils of Ancient Scripture Collection
Young Living Item # 19341

If you are a current Young Living member, hop into your Virtual Office and place an order for this collection.

If you are not a YL member, please reach out to the friend who put you in touch with this book/content. Being connected to someone who will provide you with education and answers is very important, and I'm sure that friend wants to be your "person" for oily education!

If you do not have a contact for Young Living, I would be delighted to help. Please send me an email and I'd be happy to help you place an order for this amazing collection! It is my passion to support our team with ongoing education using Young Living's oils and oil-infused products for health and wellness.

Notes

DeMoss, Nancy Leigh and Lawrence Kimbrough. Choosing Gratitude: Your Journey to Joy. Chicago: Moody Publishers, 2009.

"Four Species." Jewish Virtual Library: A Project of AICE. https://www.jewishvirtuallibrary.org/four-species 19 Dec. 2018

Leaf, Dr. Caroline. Switch on Your Brain. Grand Rapids, Baker Books, 2013.

Stewart, Dr. David. Healing Oils of the Bible. Marble Hill, MO, CARE Publications, 2015.

Strong's Exhaustive Concordance Bible Hub. https://biblehub.com/strongs.htm 19 Dec. 2018.

Young, Mary. D. Gary Young: The World Leader in Essential Oils. Lehi, UT, Young Living Essential Oils, LC, 2015.